HALL OF MIRRORS

THE DANDY

Printed and Published in Great Britain by D. C. THOMSON & CO., LTD.,
185 Fleet Street, London, EC4A 2HS.

BOOK

ISBN 0-85116-437-4

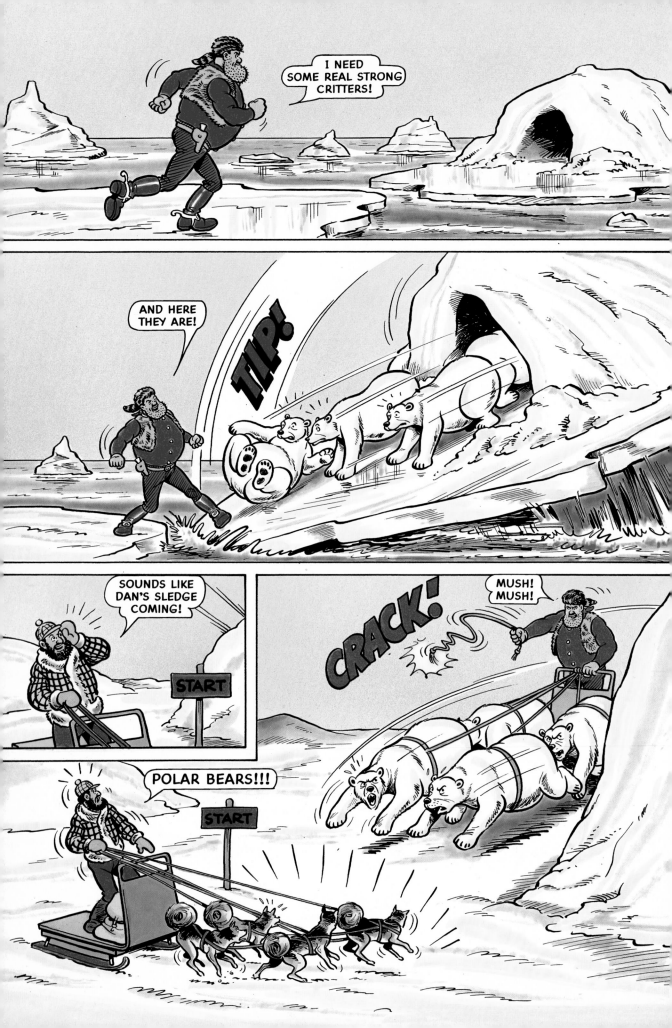

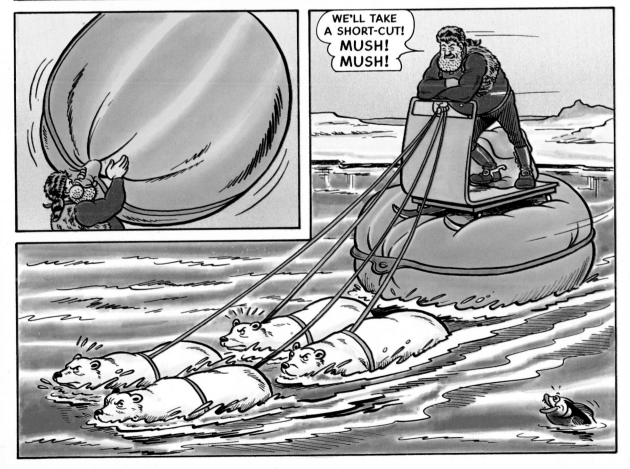

DINAH MO

KNOW WHAT I HATE?

LOTS OF THINGS!

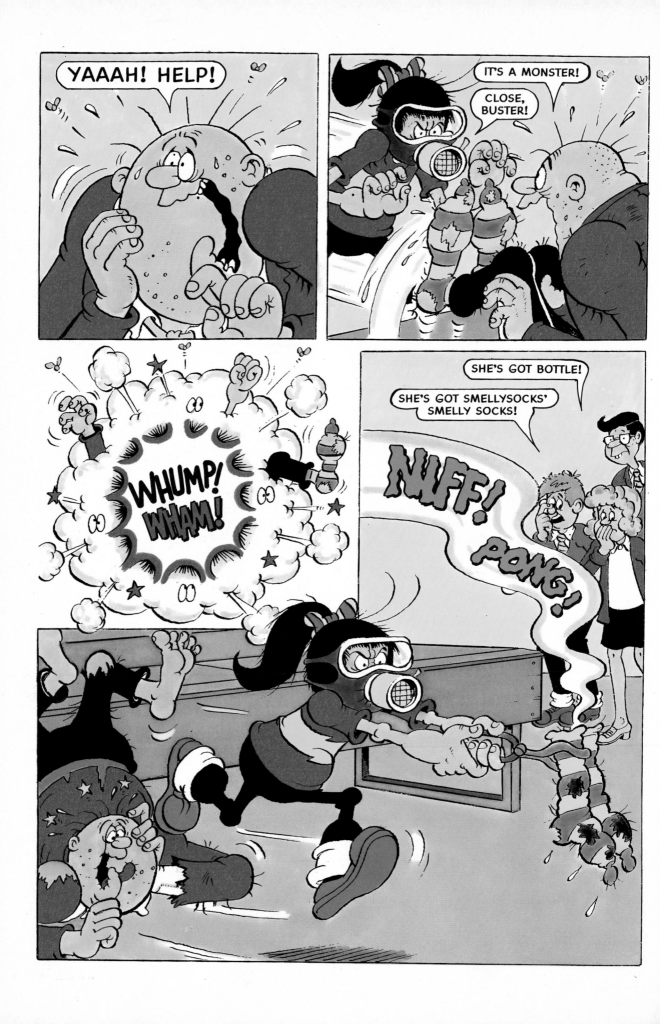

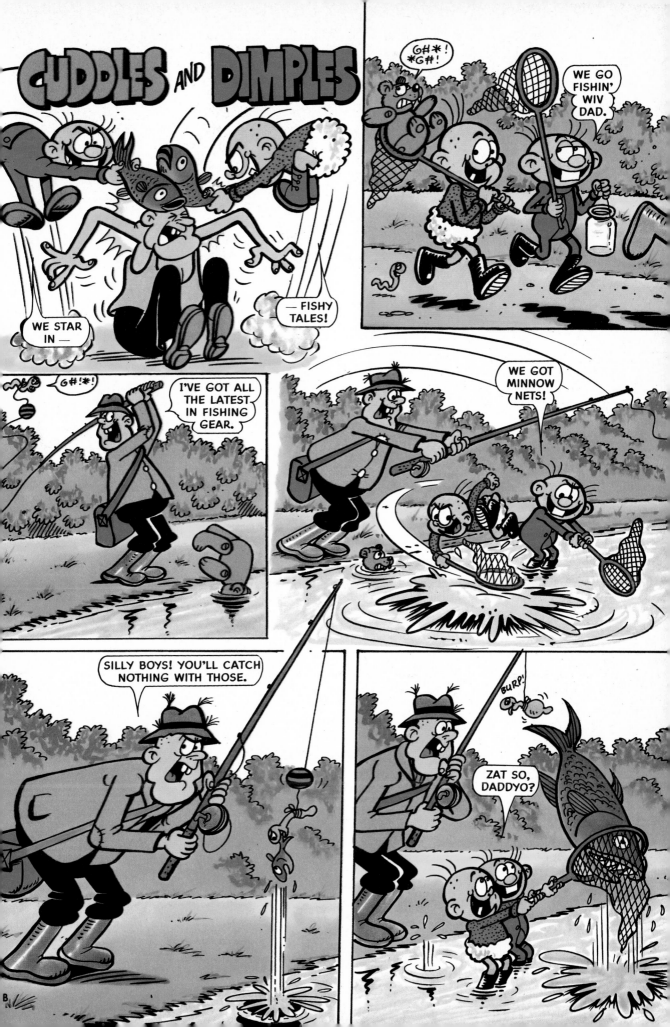

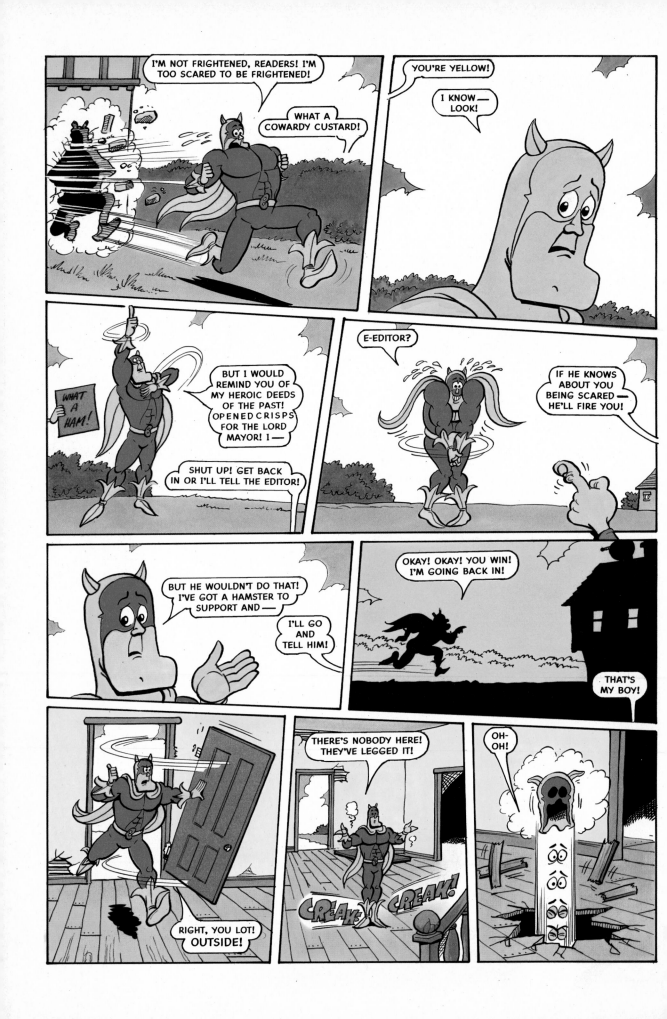

YOUNG BLACK BOB

THE hills and valleys of the Scottish borders had seemed empty with the passing of Andrew Glenn, the shepherd, and his world famous champion sheepdog, Black Bob. But now the hills echoed once again to joyous barking, for Glenn's nephew, Andy had come to live there with his own faithful collie, Young Black Bob.

LET'S HAVE A BREAK, BOB. WE'VE BEEN HERDING SHEEP ALL MORNING!

IT'S OLD TAM, THE FARMER.

HELLO, ANDY LAD! CAN YOU HELP ME?

MY TRACTOR IS STUCK IN THE MUD — THE BACK TYRES WON'T GRIP.

WHAT A CLAPPED-OUT OLD MACHINE!

Even young Bob helped to push, and soon the tractor was moving.

COME ON, BOB. HELP ME TO DRAG THIS LOG DOWN, AND PUT IT UNDER THE TRACTOR'S BACK WHEELS.

IT'S ABOUT TIME YOU GOT A NEW TRACTOR, TAM!

OCH, NO! TWO NEW BACK TYRES IS ALL SHE NEEDS, ANDY.

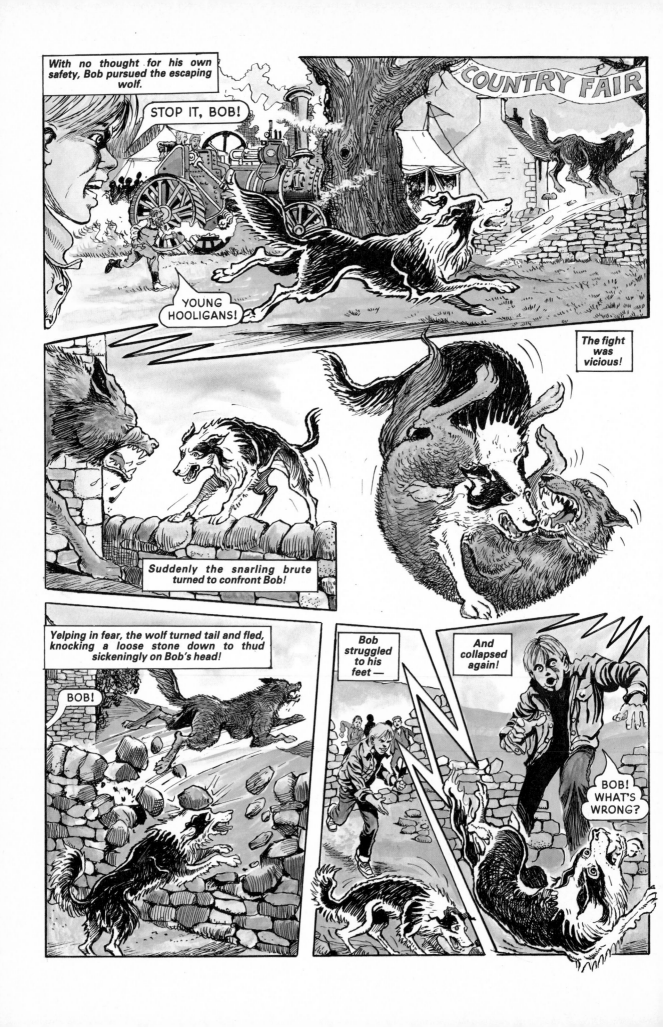

SAMMY SUPERSNAIL

— Smasher's famous pet snail!

It's 1914, and Sammy's Great-Grandad reads some terrible news in his paper, the 'Snail and Slug Gazette'—

BY GUM! BRITAIN AT WAR WI' GERMANY! VOLUNTEERS WANTED... SO IT'S COME TO THIS!

WORLD WAR ONE DECLARED

Then, slowly, along came Sammy's Grandad —

I'VE VOLUNTEERED, DAD! DON'T ARGUE WITH ME. THERE'S NOWT YOU CAN DO 'BOUT IT!

IT'LL ALL BE OVER BY CHRISTMAS.

So, off slithered the gallant 2nd Battalion of the King's Own Armoured Attack Snails, singing as they went...

IT'S A LONG WAY TO TIPPERARY, IT'S A LONG WAY TO GO!

SLITHER! CRAWL!

And they slithered, and slithered—

IT'S A LONG, LONG, LONG WAY TO TIPPERARY!

OVER BY CHRISTMAS? GROAN! DAD SAID THAT TWO YEARS AGO!

And slithered . . . and slithered . . .

WHEEZE! IT TAKES A VERY LONG TIME FOR US SNAILS TO GET TO THE FRONT!

ARE WE PAST DOVER YET?

PUFF! WHEEZE! GASP!

Brian Walker

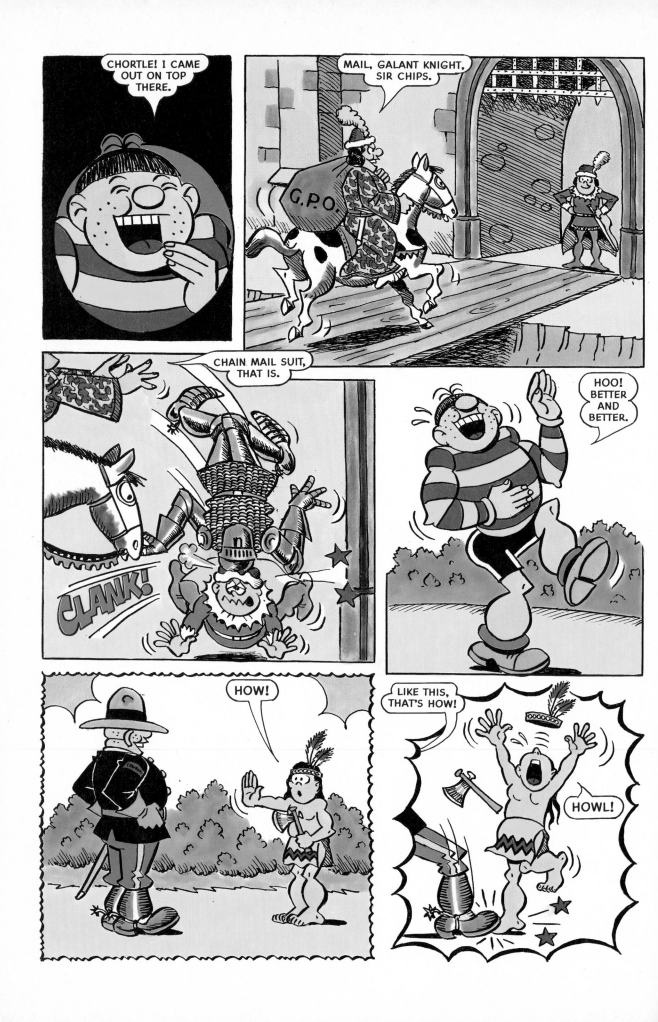

Next day—

SO I NOW DECLARE THIS YOUTH CLUB WELL AND TRULY OPEN!

AND MAY GOD HAVE MERCY ON ALL WHO ENTER HER.

AFTER YOU, VICTIM!

THESE ARE OUR YOUTH LEADERS.

PLEASED TO MEET YOU, LORD HITCHFIELD.

LET'S PLAY POOL — YOU BREAK.

WITH PLEASURE!

CRACK!

AYE! I BROKE IT ALL RIGHT!

GUFFAW!

GROAN!

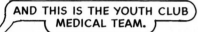

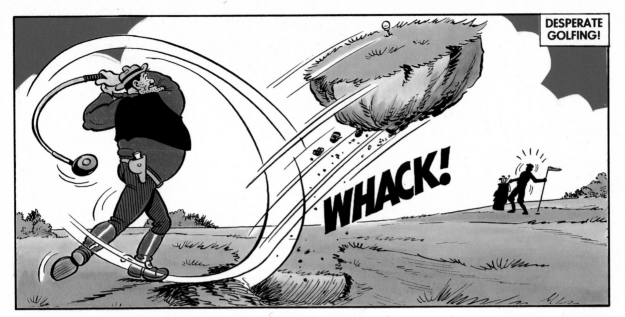

DESPERATE
GOLFING!

WHACK!

DESPERATE
JOUSTING!

DESPERATE
CANOEING!

ZOOM!

DESPERATE CLIMBING!

DESPERATE HOT-AIR BALLOONING!

DESPERATE BIRD-WATCHING!

IT'S DAD'S BIRTHDAY SO HE'S TAKING US OUT FOR NOSH! YUMMY! FISH AND CHIPS!

TONY'S FISH RESTAURANT

HEY! WHERE ARE WE GOING? TONY'S IS BACK THERE! REVERSE! REVERSE!

TONYS FISH RESTAURANT

NOT HERE!

IT'S MY BIRTHDAY! I WANT TO TRY GREEK FOOD.

GOOD DAY, PEEPS! MAY I SUGGEST MOUSSAKA?

I AIN'T AN OWL, MATE — I DON'T EAT MICE!

SILLY BOY! MOUSSAKA'S A GREEK DISH.

BUT...

HEY! IT'S JUST LIKE MINCE — AND IT'S GOOD!

I KNEW HE'D LIKE IT!

YOU LIKE MOUSSAKA, PEEPS?

SMASHING, MATE!

OOPS!

OH, NO!

WE'RE IN TROUBLE AGAIN!

SMASH!

EXCUSE, PEEPS, WHILE I PICK UP JUG!

HE'S CLEARING THE TABLE.

HE'S GOING TO THROW US OUT.

PERFECTOS!

I DON'T BELIEVE IT!

SHATTER!

HE'S SMASHED IT ON PURPOSE!

YOU MUST HAVE GREEK BLOOD IN YOU. IT IS GOOD LUCK TO SMASH PLATES WHEN YOU ARE HAPPY!

I'M HAPPY WHEN I'M SMASHING! I'M SMASHER!

YOU ARE CALLED SMASHER? THEN YOU MUST BE RELATED TO THE ANCIENT GREEK — SMASHEROPOLOUS!

BANTU

THINGS looked bad for Bantu, the chimp! the crack of a hunter's deadly gun . . .

. . . but in fact, it was all in a day's work for this highly trained star of TV commercials.

JUNGLE NIGHTS! MY FAVOURITE DARK CHOCOLATES! HOW SWEET!

GREAT WORK, BANTU!

BANTU'S ONLY INTERESTED IN GRABBING THOSE CHOCOLATES!

When filming was over, Bantu's owner, young Steve Traynor and his dad hurried over to congratulate their pet.

But inside the box . . .

SOME KIND OF GAS . . . WHAT'S GOING ON?

. . . FEELING FAINT!

Within seconds, only two sinister figures in the TV studio were still on their feet.

THE KNOCK-OUT GAS FLATTENED THE LOT! GRAB THE CHIMP!

Korky the Cat with THE KITS NIP LIP & RIP

Strange Hill School Trip

Wish I wasn't here, Eddie

WE'RE OFF ON OUR HOLS — TO A HOLIDAY CAMP.

WE'RE SHARING THIS CHALET.

LOOKS NICE AND NORMAL.

THE COFFINS LOOK NICE AND COMFY.

EEK!

That night —

'NIGHT, EDDIE. SEE YOU IN THE MORNING.

'NIGHT, WOLFIE. HOPE SO, WOLFIE.

AAAAAAAAAAA

EEK!

A fortnight later —

SIGH! TIME TO GO HOME. WHAT A GREAT HOLIDAY.

IT GETS WORSE. WE'RE GOING HOME ON THE GHOST TRAIN.

OH, NO! NOT THE GHOST TRAIN. ANYTHING BUT THE GHOST TRAIN.

GIBBER! IF WOLFIE IS SCARED OF THE GHOST TRAIN IT MUST BE REALLY BAD.

DISCREET WAFFLE

CIVILISED GAS

BLETHER TWITTER!

GENTEEL DRONE!

THIS IS HORRID, HORRID!

NEAR HYSTERICS!

CHUCKLE! MY MONSTER MATES HATE THIS NICE, NORMAL TRAIN.

ALL US DANDY STARS STILL GO TO SCHOOL, TO LEARN OUR COMIC JOB!

TROUBLE IS, AH'M GETTIN' KINDA BIG FOR MY DESK THESE DAYS!

I'LL TAKE THE ROLL-CALL NOW. BULLY BEEF?

PRESENT, SIR — AND SO IS CHIPS!

AAARGH!

ALL PRESENT, SIR! RIGHT, YOU TWO — ANY MORE OF YOUR NONSENSE...

I'LL SET THE KITS ON YOU!

ULP! LET'S BEHAVE, OLD PAL!

AND FINALLY, FREDDIE FLY? AH, YES! PRESENT!

OYAH!

BLAT!

DRRRRRRRRR

AH, LUNCH TIME ALREADY! OFF YOU GO, PUPILS!

The class of 1990!

KINGS
DANDY BOOK 1960

THE KING OF THE POLES SCORED A COUPLE OF GOALS,
AND A COUPLE OF GOALS SCORED HE.
BUT HE GOT IN A STATE AND DISCOVERED TOO. LATE
THEY WERE 'GAINST HIS OWN TEAM—TEE-HEE!

THE KING WHO'S FROM CUBA TURNED OUT WITH A TUBA,
TURNED OUT WITH A TUBA DID HE.
HE SUCKED IN THE BALL WITH NO TROUBLE AT ALL,
THEN HE SHOT IT, PLAYING DOH, RAY AND ME.

THE KING OF WALES WORE A JERSEY OF NAILS,
AND A JERSEY OF NAILS WORE HE.
TO WARD OFF ATTACKS FROM FORWARDS AND BACKS—
AND HE PUNCTURED THEM ALL MERRILEE.

THE KING OF TIBET ON THE PITCH BROUGHT HIS PET,
ON THE PITCH BROUGHT HIS PET DID HE.
SO THAT DURING THE MATCH HE KEPT UP TO SCRATCH—
HIS PET, DO YOU SEE, WAS A FLEA.

SAID THE KING OF SIAM, "REFEREE'S WHAT I AM,"
"REFEREE'S WHAT I AM," SAID HE.
BUT HE STARTED TO SWEAT, THE WHISTLE GOT WET,
AND THE MOISTURE SPROUTED THE PEA.

THE KING OF THE SWEDES WAS A MAN FOR BIG FEEDS,
AND A MAN FOR BIG FEEDS WAS HE.
BROUGHT THE GAME TO A HALT, PRODUCED PEPPER AND SALT,
AND CHEWED UP THE BALL HUNGRILEE.

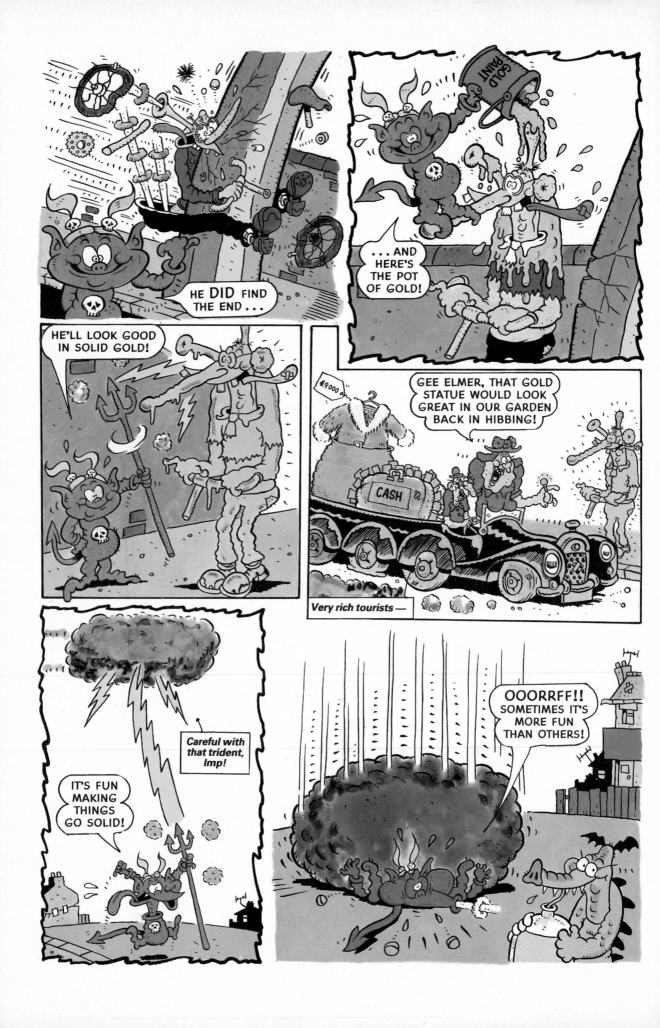

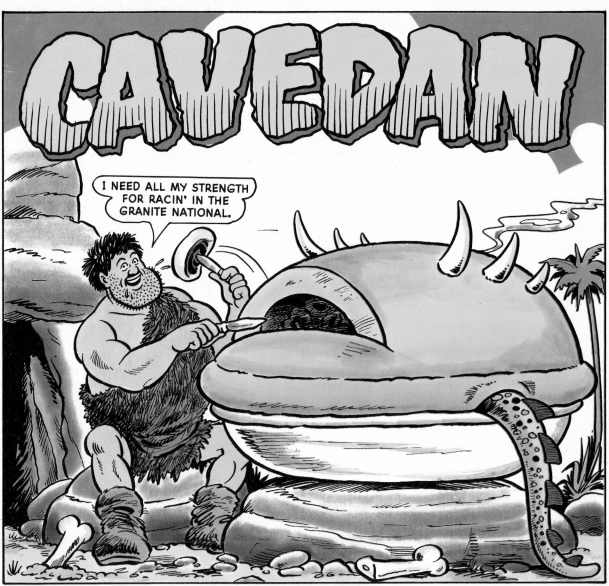

I'LL JUST HAVE A LITTLE SNACK— OH, THE PHONE.

DING!

RING!

HELLO, LITTLE ERIC SPEAKING. CAN I HELP YOU?

ERIC, IT'S ME, CHIEFY! I NEED BANANAMAN URGENTLY—LIKE RIGHT AWAY.

Back home—

KEEP A DANDY HANDY!

Follow the fun adventures of your best pals, in the DANDY every week!

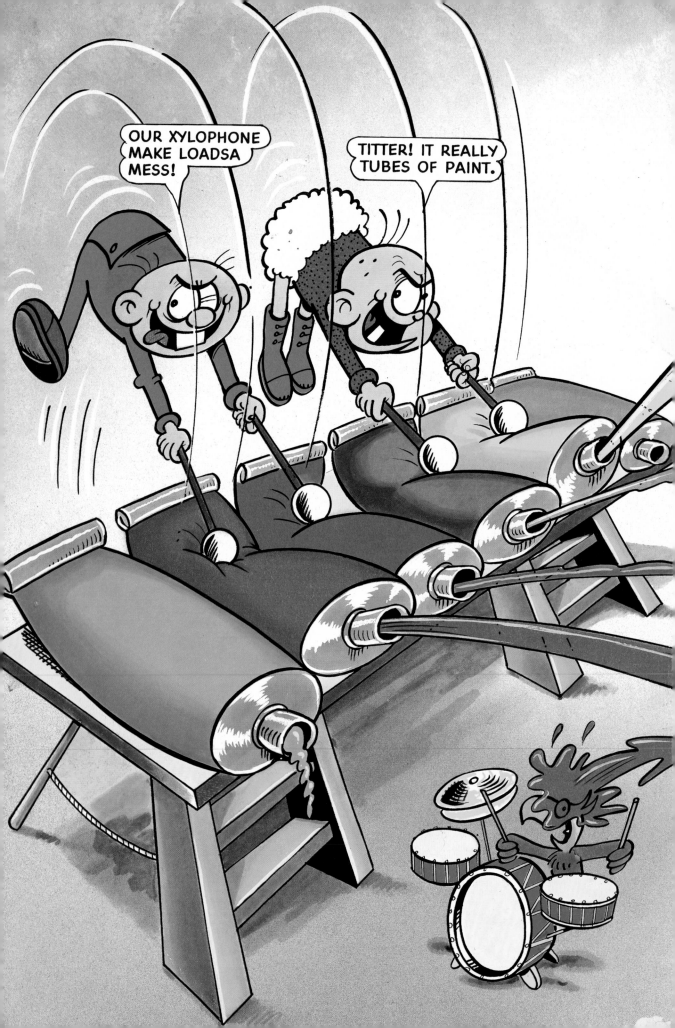